Christmas

Begins With

CHRIST

written by
Gina Kirkland

illustrated by
Marissa Napolitano

Written by Gina Kirkland

Illustrated by Marissa Napolitano

Edited by Brooke Vitale

Published by Gina Kirkland

ISBN: 979-8-9865202-0-9 - Hardcover

   979-8-9865202-1-6 - Paperback

   979-8-9865202-2-3 - Ebook

Library of Congress Control Number: 2022915781

First printing edition 2022

Printed in the USA

www.BeginsWithChrist.com

To my incredible husband and soulmate, Jimmie. To quote Emily Bronte, whatever our souls are made of, yours and mine are the same.

To our beautiful children, Gloria and Jeremy. May you always feel the unseen spiritual support around you.

You three are my daily sunshine and moon in the night.

And to Caroline, thank you for influencing me to write this book. By sharing your own light, you created a ripple effect that encouraged me to share my own.

Do you know about Christmas?
Why Santa comes here?
It's not about toys,
Or sleigh bells and reindeer.

It started with Jesus,
The source of all light.

Santa Claus needs this,
To see in the night.

Just like a great star,
That shines in the sky,
He's looking upon you,

He's always nearby.

Just like the sun,

He's wherever you go.

Just like the ocean,
More vast than you know.

Although you can't see Him,
He's there to help out.
Whenever you're lost,
He will show you the route.

Just try, you can feel Him,
While praying at night.
His love's always with you,
Embracing you tight.

He's right there to listen,
With words that will mend.
He speaks to your heart,
An invisible friend.

So Christmas is when,
We rejoice and we play!
Christmas is special.
'Cause it's His birthday!

The love that He gives us,
Lives deep inside you.

Go share it with others,
See what it can do!

Santa Claus does this,
He always spreads joy.
It makes him **so happy,**
When you get a toy.

But love can be shown,
In more ways than just this.
Let's watch how love grows,
When it starts with a **kiss.**

One mistletoe swaying,

1

Two people in love,

2

Lips coming together,
Leaves dangling above.

Then three people **skip**,

And four more join the fray.

4

Five carolers sing,

Making six **smile** today.

Then seven **rejoice,**

And eight more people **laugh.**

It all keeps on going,
'Til nine **dance** at last.

From one mistletoe,
And the love in a kiss,
Joy keeps on spreading,
To ten states of **bliss.**

10

Christmas is more,
Than a cookie or toy.

It's a day to praise Jesus—
A day to spread joy!

Remember that Christmas,
Is one day of cheer.
But you can spread love,
Every day of the year.

So go kiss and hug,
All your family and friends.
Keep smiling and caring,
For love never ends.

Jesus is watching,

He's smiling with pride.
He's right there beside you,
Your friend and your guide.

Made in the USA
Columbia, SC
06 November 2024